Assessment Tests in
Maths
for Key Stage 2

Peter Patilla

Nelson

Thomas Nelson and Sons Ltd
Nelson House Mayfield Road
Walton-on-Thames Surrey
KT12 5PL UK

Thomas Nelson Australia
102 Dodds Street
South Melbourne
Victoria 3205 Australia

Nelson Canada
1120 Birchmount Road
Scarborough Ontario
M1K 5G4 Canada

© 1993 Peter Patilla

First Published by Thomas Nelson and Sons Ltd 1993
This edition published 1995

I(T)P Thomas Nelson is an International
        Thomson Publishing Company

I(T)P is used under licence

ISBN 0-17-420271-7
NPN 9 8 7 6 5

Illustrator: Dandi Palmer

Printed in Croatia

To parents

National Curriculum Tests
The work your child studies in school is set out in the National Curriculum. This tells teachers what children should be learning at the different stages of their development throughout their school life. The first part of the curriculum, for the infant years up to age 7, is called Key Stage 1. Children then study Key Stage 2 from age 7 to 11. The subjects they study contain work at different levels of ability and schools monitor pupils' progress continuously. At the ages of 7 and 11, children take National Tests to help their teachers confirm which level of attainment they have reached. Children start school working towards level 1 and most of them should reach level 2 by the age of 7, and level 4 when they are 11.

How this book can help your child
This book is to give your child some practice in doing tests at home. Working through the exercises will help your child to see that tests are not frightening and that it can be fun to find out how much you know about a subject. The exercises will:
- Give your child practice in the security of a home environment and help him or her to feel comfortable about taking the tests.
- Provide many examples of the kinds of questions that could be set in the tests. Although they are not actual National Curriculum tests, the exercises are arranged at the various levels described in the National Curriculum.
- Enable you to estimate the level at which your child is working.

How you can help
Most of the tests are self-explanatory and once you have made sure your child understands what to do, encourage him or her to do the test quietly without help as far as possible. Each test will probably take about 30 to 40 minutes.
- Mark the tests with the help of the answers at the back of the book as soon as possible after they are completed.
- It may be useful and encouraging to your child to start off with the early tests in the book, even if you are sure he or she is working at higher levels.
- Praise success and if difficulties arise encourage your child to leave the work for a while. Above all, make the tests as enjoyable as possible.

Maths at Key Stage 2
Your child will need access to a calculator, coloured pencils, a ruler, a protractor, a pair of compasses, plain paper and scissors. He or she may also ask for tracing paper, coins or dice, so have these available if possible.

CONTENTS

Each test covers the following:
Number, Algebra, Shape and space, and Handling data.

1. Join these numbers up in order. Start with the smallest.

| 30 | | 91 | | 19 | | 53 |

| 87 | | 78 | | 46 |

Say the numbers.

2. Answer these as quickly as you can.

3 + 7 = _____   4 + 5 = _____   1 + 5 = _____   8 + 0 = _____

3. Answer these as quickly as you can.

10 – 7 = _____   9 – 5 = _____   4 – 4 = _____   6 – 0 = _____

4. Find the total cost of each shopping bag.
You can use coins to help you.

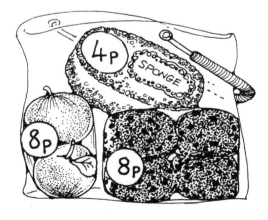

total cost _____   total cost _____

Find the change from 50p for each shopping bag.

change from 50p _____   change from 50p _____

5. Count the circles.
Colour a half.   Colour a quarter.

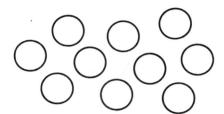   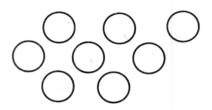

6. Choose a suitable word from the list to complete each sentence.

A tablespoon measures in _____   centimetres

Kitchen scales weigh in _____   litres

A bucket measures in _____   grams

A wristwatch measures in _____   millilitres

A ruler measures in _____   minutes

7. Suggest some numbers which might fit into: $\square - \diamond = 3$

Here is one example: $3 - 0 = 3$
Write some more.

8. Find the missing numbers in these patterns.

21, 19, 17, 15, ☐, ☐, 9, 7, 5, ☐.

8, 10, ☐, 14, ☐, 18, ☐, 22, 24.

9. Join each shape to its name.

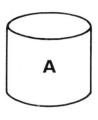

 square

cube

triangle

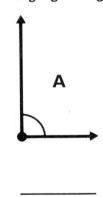 cuboid

cylinder

pentagon

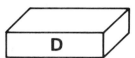

10. The little pointer turns.
How many right angles has it turned through?

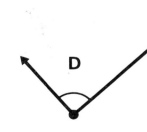

A ____

B ____

C ____

D ____

E ____

11. This graph shows some children's favourite fruit.

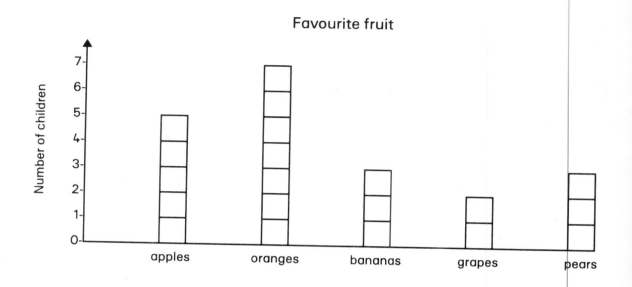

Which fruit is most popular? _____

Which fruit is least popular? _____

How many children liked pears best? _____

How many children took part in answering the question about

favourite fruit? _____

12. Which shape is in the wrong place?

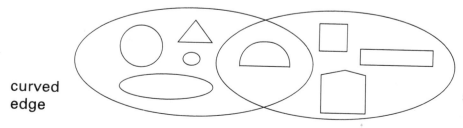

curved
edge

straight
edge

1. 32 is three tens and two units: 32 = 30+2
Write these numbers in the same way.

68 = _____   45 = _____   71 = _____   96 = _____

2. Answer these as quickly as you can.

4 + ☐ = 10   5 + ☐ = 8   ☐ + 3 = 9   ☐ + 6 = 10

3. Answer these as quickly as you can.

9 − ☐ = 2   8 − ☐ = 8   ☐ − 4 = 2   ☐ − 5 = 0

4. Find the total cost of these.
You can use coins to help you.

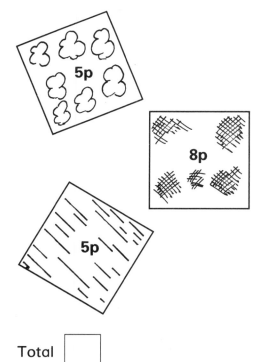

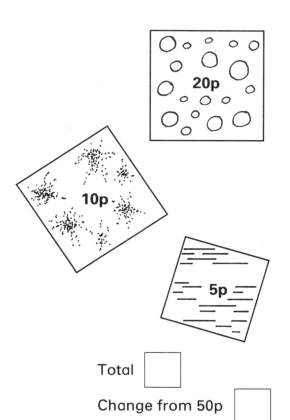

Total ☐

Change from 50p ☐

Total ☐

Change from 50p ☐

5.

Colour a half.

Colour a quarter.

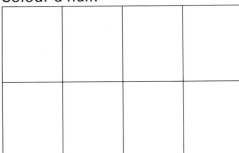

6. Write the missing numbers in these patterns.

2, 4, 6, ___ , ___ , ___ , ___ , ___

1, 3, 5, ___ , ___ , ___ , ___ , ___

Tick the even number pattern.

7. Suggest some numbers which might fit into ☐ + ◇ = 10

Here is one example 9 + 1 = 10
Write some more in the box below.

8. Chose a suitable word from the list to complete each sentence.

A tablespoon measures in _____ minutes

A clock measures in _____ millilitres

Scales measure in _____ kilograms

A bucket measures in _____ litres

9. Name these shapes.

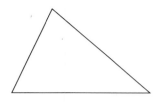  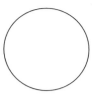

_____   _____   _____   _____

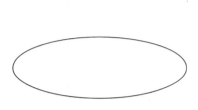 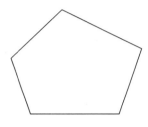 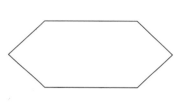

_____   _____   _____

10. Put a cross in each right angle.

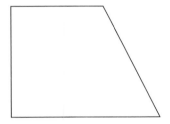 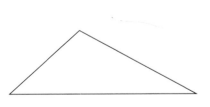 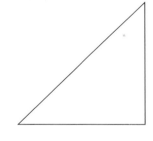

 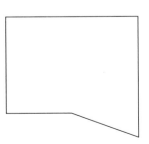 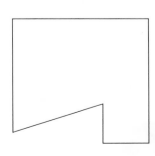

11. Here is a chart of children's birthdays.

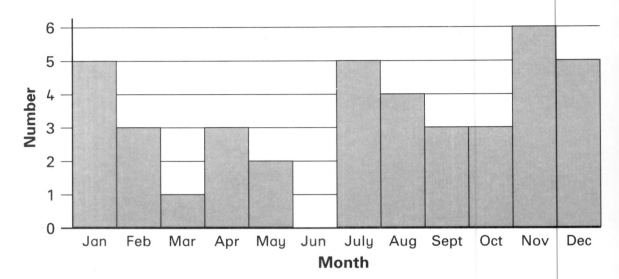

How many children have a birthday in September? _____

In which months do 5 children have their birthday? _____

12. This is a calendar for May.

MAY

Sun	Mon	Tue	Wed	Thu	Fri	Sat
	1	2	3	4	5	6
7	8	9	10	11	12	13
14	15	16	17	18	19	20
21	22	23	24	25	26	27
28	29	30	31			

Which day of the week was 9th May? _____

1. Write the number shown on each abacus.

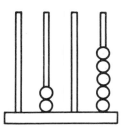   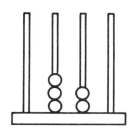   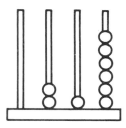

_____   _____   _____

Write the numbers in order. Start with the smallest. _____

2. Write four sums replacing △ and □ with numbers.

   △ × □ = **12**

   _____   _____   _____   _____

3. How many of these egg boxes will be needed for each set of eggs?

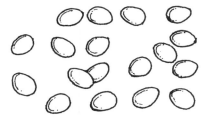      

_____   _____

How many eggs are in the partially-filled box? _____

4. You may use a calculator.
   How many of these tickets can be

   bought for £14·70? _____

STALLS   STALLS
£2·45

What would 8 of these tickets cost? _____

5. Do not use a ruler.
   Draw lines which you think are as long as:

   2cm

   8cm

   12cm

   Now use a ruler to see how good your estimates were.

   2cm _____   8cm _____   12cm _____

6. Look at the arrows and write the measurements.

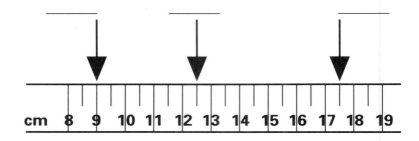

7. Here is 28 written in two different ways: $30 - 2$, $25 + 3$.
   Write each of these two numbers in four different ways.

   49 _____   _____   _____   _____

   81 _____   _____   _____   _____

8. Draw a ring round all the numbers which can be divided exactly by 5.

   45   60   95   102

       34   52   155   130

9. Look at these machines.
   Fill in the missing numbers.

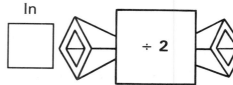

10. These shapes have been sorted.

What do they have in common?

_____

11. Tick the models which are symmetrical.

  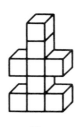

    A   **B**   **C**   **D**   **E**

12. Here is a list of entrance prices to a castle.

Entrance Prices		
	Mon-Fri	Sat-Sun
Adult	£6.50	£7.50
Child 4-14	£4.00	£5.00
Child under 4	Free	Free

What is the entrance cost for an adult on Wednesday? _____

What is the entrance cost for a 7 year old on Sunday? _____

15

13. Here is part of a train timetable.

Lipton to Domley					
Monday to Friday		Saturday		Sunday	
Lipton	Domley	Lipton	Domley	Lipton	Domley
depart	arrive	depart	arrive	depart	arrive
07.00	08.45	07.00	08.40	08.30	11.10
08.00	09.45	08.30	10.15	11.30	13.55
09.00	10.45	10.00	11.45		
10.00	11.45				
11.00	12.55				

Which train arrives in Domley at 10.15 on a Saturday? _____

Approximately how long does the journey take? _____

14. Write the time.

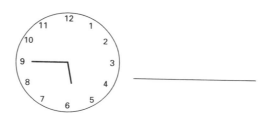 _____

15. People were asked on which day of the week their birthday came.
Draw a bar graph to show this information.

Day	Sun	Mon	Tues	Wed	Thur	Fri	Sat
Number of people	12	8	4	6	7	9	8

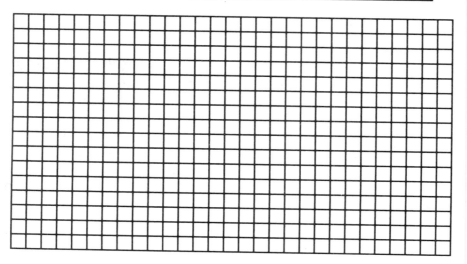

1. Draw a line from each number to show where it goes on the number line.

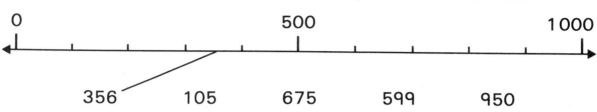

356   105   675   599   950

Say the numbers.

2. Answer these as quickly as you can.

    20 – 17 = _____   18 – 15 = _____   15 – 12 = _____

    19 – 14 = _____   20 – 16 = _____   17 – 13 = _____

3.   Oranges cost 10p each.
    What would 6 oranges cost? _____

     5 lemons cost 45p.
    What would one lemon cost? _____

    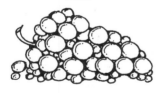 Grapes cost 60p a pound.
    What would half a pound cost? _____

4. How much is in each set?

    _____   _____

5. Do not use a ruler.
Draw lines which you think are as long as:

2cm

6cm

10cm

Now use a ruler to see how good your estimates were. Write good, fair or poor

2cm _____   6cm _____   10cm _____

6. How many seconds have passed on each of these stopwatches?

_____   _____   _____

7. Write the next two numbers in each pattern.
Try to predict what the tenth number in each pattern will be.

1, 2, 3, 1, 2, 3, _____   the tenth number will be _____

14, 24, 34, 44, 54, _____   the tenth number will be _____

8. Divide each number by 10 and write down the remainder.

25 ⟶ remainder _____   72 ⟶ remainder _____   97 ⟶ remainder _____

9. Look at these machines.
Fill in the missing numbers.

In  × 5 Out   In 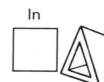 ÷ 2 Out

9

9

18

10. Use colour to sort these shapes into three sets.

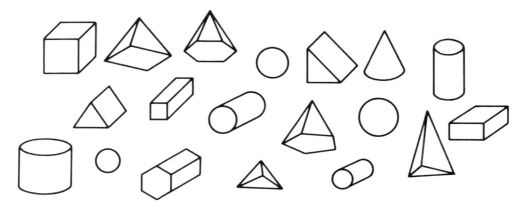

Colour of set   What the set has in common

_____   _____

_____   _____

_____   _____

11. Use three colours to make a symmetrical pattern.

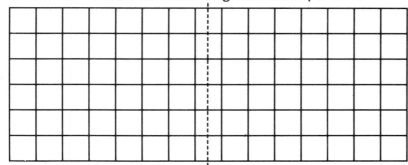

12. Draw a hexagon in the box.

13.

Petro's Ices	
Small cornet	30p
Large cornet	45p
Wafer	35p
Choc ice	60p
Tub	50p
Ice lolly	30p

Jean's Iceparlour	
Small cornet	34p
Large cornet	42p
Wafer	35p
Choc ice	60p
Tub	55p
Ice lolly	28p

Who sells the cheaper ice lolly? _____

How much would two choc ices from Jean's Iceparlour cost? _____

What would a tub and a wafer cost from Petro's Ices? _____

14. This graph shows how many cars passed by a school between 10am and 11am during one week.

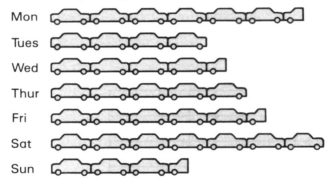

Cars passing a school between 10am and 11am

= 10 cars

= less than 10 cars

How many cars passed by on Friday? _____

On which day did between 30 and 40 cars pass by? _____

Which was the busiest day? _____

15. Make the clock show 3.30

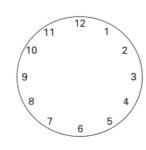

1. Here are three cards.

$$\boxed{1} \quad \boxed{4} \quad \boxed{7}$$

Which 3-digit numbers can you make with these cards?

417, _____

Write the numbers in order.

_____

Say the numbers.

2. Answer these as quickly as you can.

$8 + 7 =$ _____ $9 + 5 =$ _____ $6 + 8 =$ _____ $7 + 7 =$ _____

$12 - 5 =$ _____ $14 - 8 =$ _____ $17 - 9 =$ _____ $19 - 9 =$ _____

3. Answer these as quickly as you can.

$2 \times 8 =$ _____ $5 \times 5 =$ _____ $4 \times 3 =$ _____ $10 \times 8 =$ _____

$7 \times 2 =$ _____ $10 \times 6 =$ _____ $7 \times 5 =$ _____ $4 \times 4 =$ _____

4. You may use a calculator.
A car travels 33 miles on 1 gallon of petrol.

How far will it travel on 6 gallons of petrol? _____

How many gallons will it need to travel 264 miles? _____

5. Write these numbers to the nearest 10.

$38 \longrightarrow$ _____ $56 \longrightarrow$ _____ $72 \longrightarrow$ _____ $97 \longrightarrow$ _____

Write these numbers to the nearest 100.

$174 \longrightarrow$ _____ $329 \longrightarrow$ _____ $543 \longrightarrow$ _____ $681 \longrightarrow$ _____

6. Look at this sum. It is shown on the number line.

$$4 - 6 = {}^-2$$

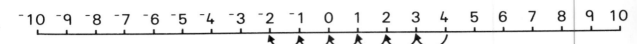

Do the same with these sums.

$$5 - 7 = \boxed{}$$

Do the same with these sums.

$$2 - 8 = \boxed{}$$

7. Work these out in your head and write the answers.

31 + 28 = _____   42 + 36 = _____   16 + 62 = _____

45 − 21 = _____   95 − 21 = _____   68 − 53 = _____

Say how you worked them out.

8. Tick the even numbers.

56   70   83   66   25   120   154   170

Underline the numbers which can be divided exactly by 5.

9. Four has been taken away from some numbers to leave these answers.

8   10   13   16

What were the starting numbers? _____

Six has been added to some numbers to give these answers.

9   12   15   20

What were the starting numbers? _____

10. Use colour to sort these shapes into three sets.

Colour of set   What the set has in common

_____   _____

_____   _____

_____   _____

11. Look at these shapes.

A   B   C   D   E

Which of the shapes do not have a line of symmetry? _____

12. Draw lines to show where each shape fits on the diagram.

	curved	not curved
symmetrical		
not symmetrical		

23

13. Here are the results of some sports teams.

	Played	HOME			AWAY			Points
		W	D	L	W	D	L	
Rockets	20	9	1	0	6	2	2	48
Jacks	21	8	2	0	6	5	0	49
Lifers	21	7	2	2	2	4	4	33
Jinglies	19	4	2	3	2	4	4	24
Nelsons	20	2	6	3	2	0	7	18
Polywebs	20	2	2	5	1	2	8	13

W = games won D = games drawn L = games lost

Which team has lost most away games? _____

Which team has scored 33 points? _____

Which team has not lost a game? _____

14. Here is a graph showing children's birthdays.

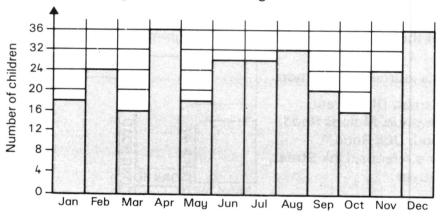

How many children have a birthday in October? _____

Which months have most birthdays? _____

Which month has 32 birthdays in it? _____

15. Write the time on the digital watch.

1. These numbers can be added together to make 3 427.

    | 400 | 3 000 | 7 | 20 |

    What will these two sets of numbers make?

    | 70 | 200 | 5 | 6 000 | _____

    | 20 000 | 300 | 9 | 60 | 5 000 | _____

    Say the numbers.

2. Answer these as quickly as you can.

    8 × 7 = _____   9 × 9 = _____   8 × 8 = _____   6 × 8 = _____

    9 × 6 = _____   7 × 4 = _____   9 × 7 = _____   7 × 7 = _____

3. Add these without using a calculator.

    ```
      345          673          208          195
    + 546        + 298        + 567        +336
    -----        -----        -----        -----
      891          971          775
    ```

4. Do not use a calculator.
    A small bag of mixed nuts costs 19p.

    How many bags can be bought for £4? _____

    What will the change be? _____

    How much will 4 bags cost? _____

5. You may use a calculator.
    Three lengths are cut from a 12 metre length of wood.
    The three lengths are 1·40m, 3·05m and 2·35m.

    What length of wood remains? _____

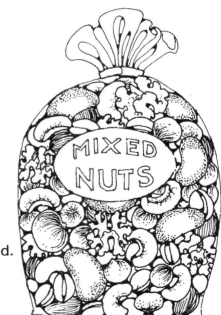

25

6. Colour $\frac{3}{4}$ of each set.

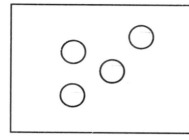 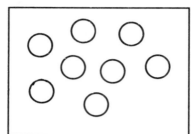 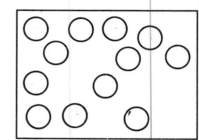

7. 1 metre = _____ cm   1 kilogram = _____ g

1 centimetre = _____ mm   1 litre = _____ ml

8. How many squares will be in the next shape? _____

  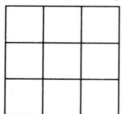 ?

How many squares do you think will be in the eighth shape? _____

9. Look at this machine.

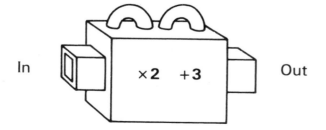

In   ×2   +3   Out

Complete the table.

In	Out
2	7
5	
	17

10. Draw a ring round all the obtuse angles in these shapes.

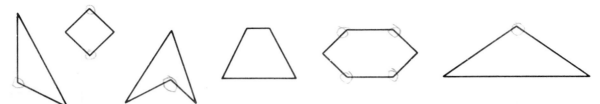

11. Look at this town plan.

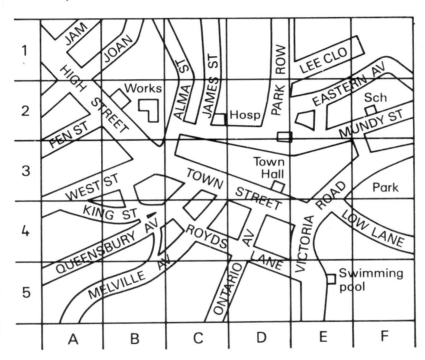

Which building can be found in D3? _____

Which square shows Mundy Street School? _____

12. You can use tracing paper to help you.
Which of these shapes have rotational symmetry? _____

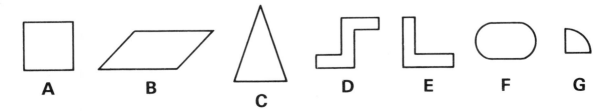

A   B   C   D   E   F   G

13. Measure the perimeters of these shapes in centimetres.

 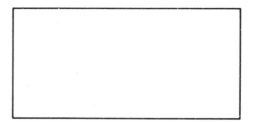 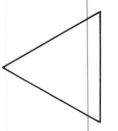

Perimeter = _____ cm   Perimeter = _____ cm   Perimeter = _____ cm

14. You may use a calculator.
Which height is the middle height of the these people?

15. Write these events in order. Start with the event which is most likely to happen to you and end with the one which is least likely.

fly to the moon   ●   go on holiday   ●   make my own bed   ●   have a meal

_____

_____

1. Write these numbers in order. Start with the smallest.

   30 050   30 500   30 005   35 000

   _____

   Say the numbers.

2. Answer these as quickly as you can.

   $8 \times 7 =$ _____ $9 \times 4 =$ _____ $3 \times 9 =$ _____ $6 \times 9 =$ _____

   $75 \times 10 =$ _____ $123 \times 10 =$ _____ $350 \times 10 =$ _____

3. Subtract these without using a calculator.

4 0 7	8 0 5	5 7 0	9 1 2
− 1 6 2	− 7 5 8	− 2 1 9	− 3 7 9

4. Work these out in your head and write the answers.
   How much heavier is one parcel than the other?

   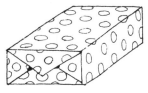    

   750g   480g   54oz   65oz

   _____   _____

5. Use a calculator.
   200 sheets of card make a pile 597mm high.
   To the nearest millimetre find:

   the thickness of 1 sheet _____

   the thickness of 564 sheets _____

6. What is 50% of each amount?

_____   _____   _____

7. Measure each line as accurately as you can.

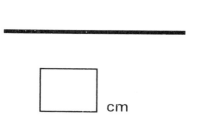 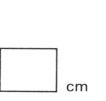 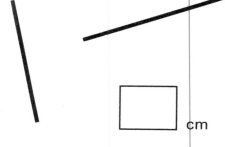

cm   cm   cm

8. What is this machine doing to each number? _____

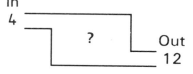  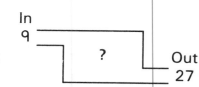

If 15 and 21 came out of the machine, which two numbers went in?

_____ and _____

9. I double a number and then add seven.
The answer is 23.
What is the number? _____

I subtract 2 from a number and then multiply it by three.
The answer is 9.
What is the number? _____

10. Tick the shapes which are identical.

 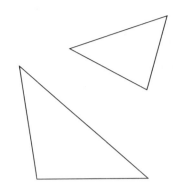 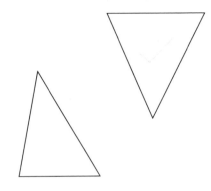

11. Write down the coordinates of each letter.

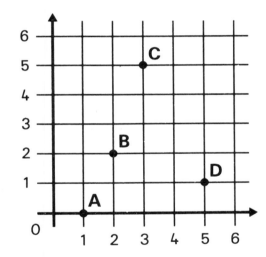

A → _____

B → _____

C → _____

D → _____

12. Which of these letters have rotational symmetry? _____

M   X   A

S   H   Z

31

13. Which of these leaves has the largest area? _____

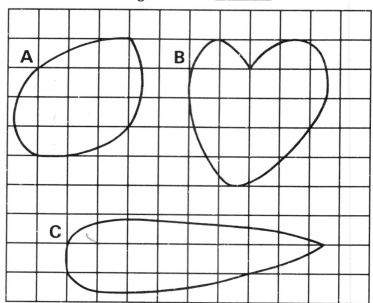

14. Measure the perimeters of these shapes.

_____   _____

15. Write some words to describe the chance of these events happening to you.

Learning to drive   Going to the moon

_____   _____

_____   _____

1. Look at how this number has been written.

$$32\,678 = 30\,000 + 2\,000 + 600 + 70 + 8$$

Write these numbers in the same way.

$51\,206 = $ _____

$213\,520 = $ _____

$723\,525 = $ _____

2. Answer these as quickly as you can.

$9 + 7 + 6 = $ _____ $4 + 7 + 5 + 6 = $ _____ $8 + 8 + 6 + 4 = $ _____

$8 \times 6 = $ _____ $7 \times 9 = $ _____ $8 \times 7 = $ _____ $4 \times 9 = $ _____

3. Do not use a calculator.

$$\begin{array}{r} 2\ 6\ 7 \\ +\ 8\ 4\ 5 \\ \hline \end{array} \qquad \begin{array}{r} 8\ 6\ 1 \\ -\ 2\ 6\ 5 \\ \hline \end{array} \qquad \begin{array}{r} 6\ 2\ 5 \\ +\ 3\ 9\ 8 \\ \hline \end{array} \qquad \begin{array}{r} 7\ 0\ 0 \\ -\ 4\ 7\ 4 \\ \hline \end{array}$$

4. Do not use a calculator.
   How many 22p stamps can be bought for £5? _____

   What will the change be? _____

   What would twelve 19p stamps cost? _____

5. You may use a calculator.
   How many 47-seater coaches will be needed to carry 296 people? _____

6. Multiply by 10   37   108   340

      _____   _____   _____

Multiply by 100   25   80   203

      _____   _____   _____

7. $\begin{array}{r} 2.34 \\ + 1.75 \\ \hline \end{array}$ $\begin{array}{r} 3.04 \\ - 1.85 \\ \hline \end{array}$

8. Here are some multiplication grids.
Fill in the missing numbers.

9	12	15	18
12	16	20	24

35	40		50
42		54	60

16		24	28
20	25		35

36		48	54
42	49	56	

9. Look at this machine.

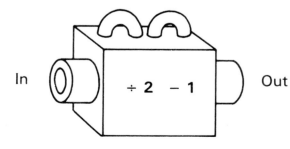

In   ÷ 2 − 1   Out

Complete the table.

In	Out
8	3
	7
20	

10. These two shapes are identical. They are the same size.

These two shapes are not identical. They are not the same size.

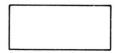

Tick the identical shapes.

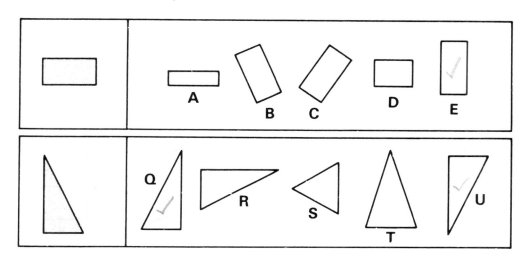

11. Put these points on the grid and join them up in order.

$(1,6) \rightarrow (3,6) \rightarrow (3,3) \rightarrow (6,3) \rightarrow (6,0) \rightarrow (5,0) \rightarrow (5,2) \rightarrow (3,2) \rightarrow (3,0) \rightarrow (2,0) \rightarrow (2,5) \rightarrow (1,5) \rightarrow (1,6)$

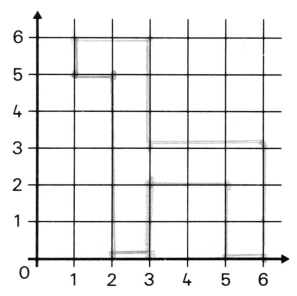

12. Where do these shapes go on the Venn diagram? Write them in.

A   B   C   D   E

C   B   A   D E

has rotational symmetry   has line symmetry

13. How many cubes were used to make these solid cuboids?

A 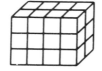   B 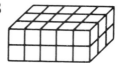   C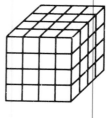

_____   _____   _____

14. Write an event for each box.

certain to happen	could happen	could not possibly happen

15. Here is a bar graph to show the number of sandwiches sold each weekday.

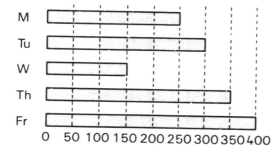

How many sandwiches were sold on Wednesday?

_____

On which day were 350 sandwiches sold?

_____

1. Join each number to a box.

| more than 1 million | between a hundred thousand and a million | between ten thousand and a hundred thousand | less than ten thousand |

2 500 000   340 540   23 560   9456

23 560   2 500 000   340 540   9456

2. Work out an approximate answer to each problem.

326 + 785

Approximately 300 + 800 → 1 100

714 + 288   896 + 921

Approximately [   ] + [   ] → _____   [   ] + [   ] → _____

3. Do not use a calculator.

6⟌84   4⟌76   5⟌95   23 × 6   45 × 3   52 × 7

4. Write each mark as a percentage.

 $\frac{5}{10}$

 $\frac{3}{10}$ $\frac{9}{10}$

 $\frac{10}{20}$

50%   _____   _____   _____

5. You may use a calculator.
You buy four books which cost £7·95, £6·25, £3·99 and £17·45.
How much change will you receive if you pay with two £20 notes? _____

6. Here is a picture of a centimetre tape measure.
Which measurements are the arrows pointing to?
Write each measurement in metres, such as 1·45m.

_____   _____

↓   ↓

| | | | | | | | | | | | | | | | | | | | | | | | | | | | | | | | | | | | | | | | | | | | | | | | |
| 10 | 20 | 30 | 40 | 50 | 60 | 70 | 80 | 90 | 1m | 110 | 120 | 130 | 140 | 150 | 160 | 170 |

7. Answer these as quickly as you can.

$9 \times 4 =$ _____ $8 \times 4 =$ _____ $7 \times 6 =$ _____ $8 \times 8 =$ _____

$7 \times 100 =$ _____ $15 \times 100 =$ _____ $45 \times 100 =$ _____

8. What do you think is happening in this pattern?
Use words or numbers to explain.

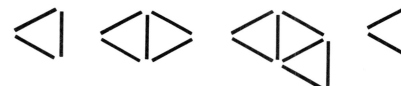

_____

_____

9. Look at this operation arrow.

When the arrow is reversed the operation changes.

Write the new operations on these arrows.

$2 \xrightarrow{(\times\ 4\ +\ 2)} 10$

$2 \xleftarrow{(-\ 2\ \div\ 4)} 10$

$4 \xrightarrow{(\times\ 2\ -\ 1)} 7$ $15 \xrightarrow{(\div\ 3\ +\ 1)} 6$ $10 \xrightarrow{(-\ 5\ \times\ 2)} 10$

$4 \longleftarrow 7$ $15 \longleftarrow 6$ $10 \longleftarrow 10$

10. Use a pair of compasses and a ruler.
Draw each reflection as accurately as you can.

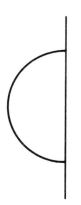 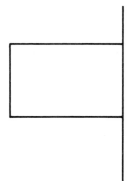

11. The coordinate at the centre of the circle is (2,3).

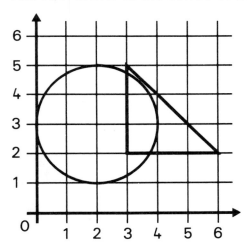

Which coordinate is both inside the triangle and touching the circle?

_____

Which coordinates are both inside the circle and touching the triangle?

_____

12. Tick the shapes which have rotational symmetry.

A   C   E

B    D   F

13. Draw three different-sized rectangles which each have **24** squares inside them.
Find the perimeter of each one and write it inside the rectangle.

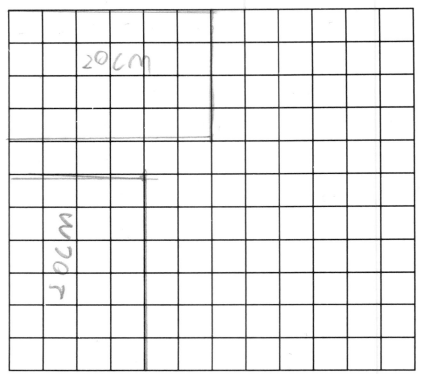

20 cm

70 cm

14. This is a graph showing a car journey.

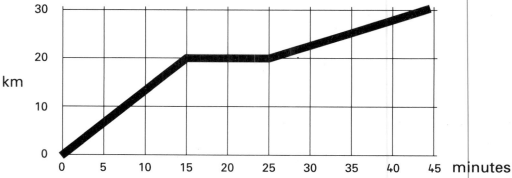

km

How long was the car stationary? _____

15. Roll two dice.
What is the chance of rolling a total of 8?
Tick which:

        certain   very likely   fair

1. Do not use a calculator.

$$\begin{array}{r} 2\,3\,6 \\ \times\ \ \ 2\,4 \\ \hline \end{array}$$
$$\begin{array}{r} 4\,6\,3 \\ \times\ \ \ 1\,8 \\ \hline \end{array}$$
$$\begin{array}{r} 3\,9\,6 \\ \times\ \ \ 3\,6 \\ \hline \end{array}$$
$$\begin{array}{r} 5\,2\,7 \\ \times\ \ \ 4\,7 \\ \hline \end{array}$$

2. Do these in your head and write the answers.

$800 \div 40 =$ _____ $600 \div 20 =$ _____ $900 \div 30 =$ _____ $500 \div 10 =$ _____

3. You may use a calculator.

$\frac{1}{10}$ of 3 metres = _____
$\frac{3}{4}$ of £6 = _____

$\frac{3}{5}$ of 2 kilograms = _____
$\frac{1}{8}$ of 2 litres = _____

4. Round these numbers off to the nearest 100.

   23 745   6 902   12 298   56 250

_____   _____   _____   _____

Round these numbers off to the nearest 1 000.

   43 678   8 199   99 786   456 498

_____   _____   _____   _____

5. Write a suitable number in each sentence.

One foot is approximately _____ centimetres.

One kilogram is approximately _____ pounds.

Eight kilometres is approximately _____ miles.

6. Example: $4^2 = 4 \times 4 = 16$. Do these in the same way.

$2^2 =$ _____
$3^2 =$ _____

$5^2 =$ _____
$6^2 =$ _____

7. Cross off 1.
Cross off all multiples of 2 except 2.
Cross off all multiples of 3 except 3.
Cross off all multiples of 5 except 5.
Cross off all multiples of 7 except 7.

Write the uncrossed numbers.

_____

_____

_____

_____

What are these numbers called?

Prime numbers

1	2	3	4	5	6	7	8	9	10
11	12	13	14	15	16	17	18	19	20
21	22	23	24	25	26	27	28	29	30
31	32	33	34	35	36	37	38	39	40
41	42	43	44	45	46	47	48	49	50
51	52	53	54	55	56	57	58	59	60
61	62	63	64	65	66	67	68	69	70
71	72	73	74	75	76	77	78	79	80
81	82	83	84	85	86	87	88	89	90
91	92	93	94	95	96	97	98	99	100

8. Write down the square root of each of these numbers.

$\sqrt{9}$ = _____ $\sqrt{25}$ = _____ $\sqrt{81}$ = _____ $\sqrt{100}$ = _____

9. Fill in the missing numbers in these fractions.

$\dfrac{1}{2} = \dfrac{3}{\Box}$ $\dfrac{2}{3} = \dfrac{\Box}{6}$ $\dfrac{3}{4} = \dfrac{15}{\Box}$ $\dfrac{3}{10} = \dfrac{\Box}{100}$ $\dfrac{4}{5} = \dfrac{12}{\Box}$

10. Find the area and the perimeter of this rectangle.

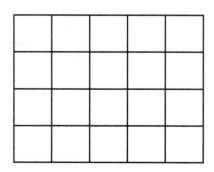

Area _____

Perimeter _____

11.

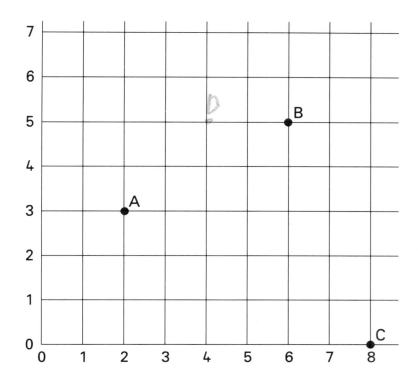

Write the co-ordinates of A _____   B _____   C _____
Put D at 4,5.

12. Draw all the lines of symmetry on each shape.
Count how many lines of symmetry each shape has.

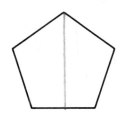

_1_ lines of symmetry

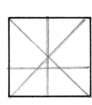

_4_ lines of symmetry

_1_ lines of symmetry

_3_ lines of symmetry

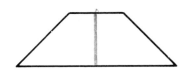

_1_ lines of symmetry

_2_ lines of symmetry

13.

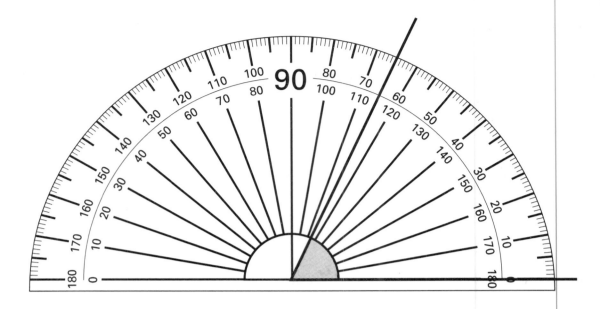

How many degrees does this angle measure? _____

14. Here is a graph to help you change miles into kilometres.

5 miles = _____ km

9 miles = _____ km

6km = _____ miles

17km = _____ miles

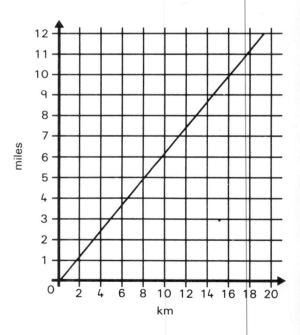

15. There are 52 playing cards in a pack.
They have been shuffled and placed face down.
Circle the chance of turning over:

any red card $\frac{1}{2}$ $\frac{1}{4}$ $\frac{1}{13}$ $\frac{1}{52}$ a club $\frac{1}{2}$ $\frac{1}{4}$ $\frac{1}{13}$ $\frac{1}{52}$

the queen of diamonds $\frac{1}{2}$ $\frac{1}{4}$ $\frac{1}{13}$ $\frac{1}{52}$

44

1. Do not use a calculator.

$14 \overline{\smash{)}3\ 6\ 4}$ $23 \overline{\smash{)}5\ 2\ 9}$ $46 \overline{\smash{)}8\ 2\ 8}$ $35 \overline{\smash{)}5\ 6\ 0}$

2. Do these in your head and write the answers.

$70 \times 50 =$ _____ $300 \times 40 =$ _____ $200 \times 400 =$ _____

3. You may use a calculator.

10% of £5 = _____   25% of 128 = _____   60% of 250g = _____

4. Write these numbers to two decimal places.

4·4572 _____   0·245 _____   12·5748 _____   3·1952 _____

Write these numbers to one decimal place.

2·5098 _____   1·992 _____   10·045 _____   8·161 _____

5. 1·2m = _____ cm   2·5cm = _____ mm   1·5km = _____ m

2·75kg = _____ g   2·25l = _____ ml 20cl = _____ ml

6. By how much has the temperature dropped?

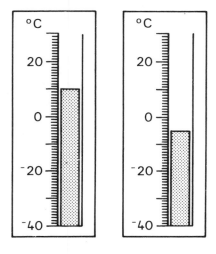

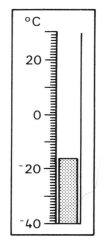

temperature drop = _____   temperature drop = _____

7. How many spots in the next pattern? _____

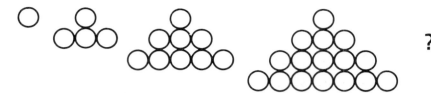

How many spots in the tenth pattern? _____

What is this sequence of numbers called? _____

8. Here are some members of the half family.
Write the next two members of the
half family.

| $\frac{1}{2}$ | $\frac{2}{4}$ | $\frac{3}{6}$ | $\frac{4}{8}$ | $\frac{5}{10}$ | $\frac{6}{12}$ |

Write the next four members of the three-quarters family.

| $\frac{3}{4}$ | $\frac{6}{8}$ | $\frac{9}{12}$ | $\frac{12}{16}$ | $\frac{15}{20}$ |

9. Example: The price of n cakes when one cake costs 25p is $25 \times n$.

The price of y stamps when one stamp costs 18p is _____

If w stamps cost 46p, then one stamp will cost _____

The total of q cakes each costing z pence will be _____

10. Calculate the volume of each shape.

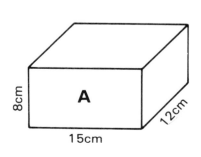

A

8cm

15cm

12cm

volume = _____

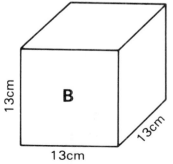

B

13cm

13cm

13cm

volume = _____

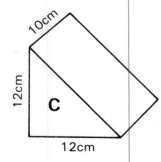

C

10cm

12cm

12cm

volume = _____

46

11. Put these points on the grid and join them up in order.

($^-$4,5)→($^-$2,4)→(2,4)→(4,5)→(4,$^-$3)→(0,$^-$5)→($^-$4,$^-$3)→($^-$4,5)

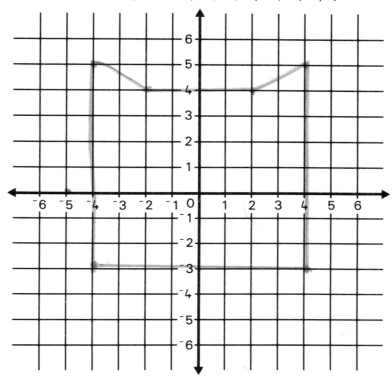

12. Use a protractor to measure the size of each angle.

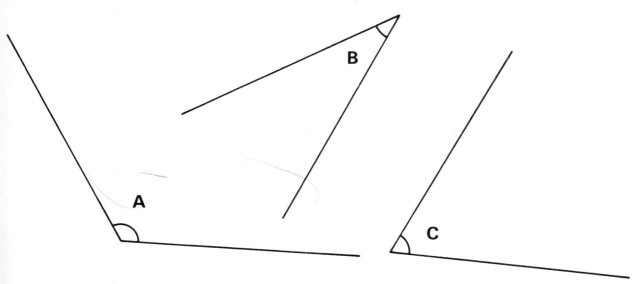

A = _____   B = _____   C = _____

13. Draw all the lines of symmetry on each shape.

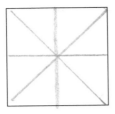

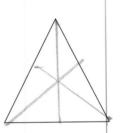

14. This pie chart shows the types of vehicles which passed a school between noon and 13.00 hours.

Were there more lorries than buses or about

the same? _____

Which was the most common vehicle to pass? _____

Did more lorries and vans pass than cars? _____

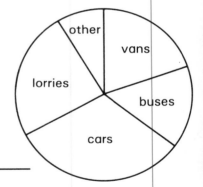

15. A dice is rolled.
Draw a ring round the chance of:

rolling a six $\frac{1}{6}$ $\frac{2}{6}$ $\frac{3}{6}$ $\frac{4}{6}$ $\frac{5}{6}$ $\frac{6}{6}$ rolling a one $\frac{1}{6}$ $\frac{2}{6}$ $\frac{3}{6}$ $\frac{4}{6}$ $\frac{5}{6}$ $\frac{6}{6}$

rolling an even number $\frac{1}{6}$ $\frac{2}{6}$ $\frac{3}{6}$ $\frac{4}{6}$ $\frac{5}{6}$ $\frac{6}{6}$

1. Do not use a calculator.

What would 144 tins cost? _____

What would 1 pen cost? _____

2. Work these out in your head and write the answers.

$500 \times 50 =$ _____ $40 \times 40 =$ _____ $800 \div 40 =$ _____

3. You may use a calculator.

$\frac{2}{3}$ of £12·42 = _____   12% of £24·50 = _____

$\frac{4}{5}$ of £16·25 = _____   15% of £60·00 = _____

4. Estimate what the missing number should be in each problem.
Use a calculator to check your estimate.
Estimate again and check.
See how many estimates you need before finding the right answer.

☐% of £265 = £39·75

estimate	check

12% of £☐ = £15·00

estimate	check

5.

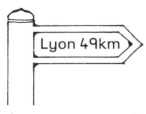

1·5 litres

$\frac{1}{4}$ kilogram

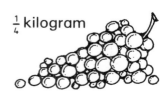

Approx. _____ miles   Approx. _____ pints   Approx. _____ ounces

6. Here are some very cold temperatures recorded in different parts of the world.

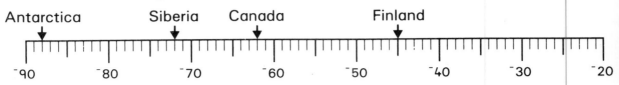

Which was the coldest place? _____

How much colder was Siberia than Canada? _____

How much colder was Canada than Finland? _____

7. Here is a diagram which changes numbers.

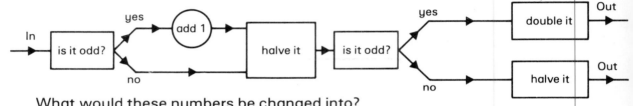

What would these numbers be changed into?

15 → _____   18 → _____   31 → _____   24 → _____

8. 6^2 = _____ 7^2 = _____

$\sqrt{25}$ = _____ $\sqrt{81}$ = _____

9.
```
  4.25        4.03
+ 3.65      - 2.85
 _____      _____
```

```
  2.15
x    5      3 ) 8.16
 _____
```

10. Use a ruler, protractor, sharp pencil and scissors.
On plain paper draw this net as accurately as you can.

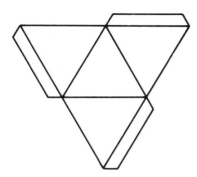

The angles are 60°.
The sides of the triangles are 65mm.
The tabs can be any sensible size.

This net is smaller than a full-sized one.

Cut out the net, score along the lines, and fold it to make a tetrahedron.

11. Each shape is rotated to fit into its outline.
How many ways will each shape fit?

      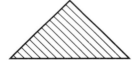   

_____   _____   _____

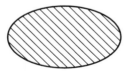   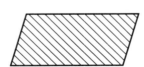   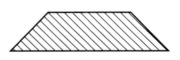

_____   _____   _____

12. 12 inches is approximately _____ cm.

1 pint is approximately _____ litres.

13. Three coins are tossed in the air together.
Make a list of all the possible ways they could land.
The order of the coins does not matter.

T   T   T

14. Here is a scale to convert between Centigrade and Fahrenheit temperatures.

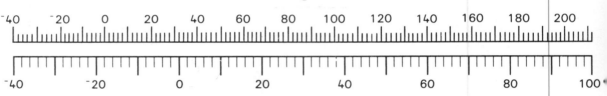

Complete the table.

°F	⁻40	32		140	
°C	⁻40		10		100

15.

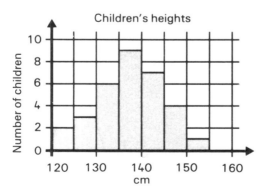

How many children are between 125 and 130cm tall? _____

How many children are taller than 140cm? _____

How many children are between 130 and 150cm tall? _____

1. Divide each number by 100.

530   40   3410

_____   _____   _____

2. Multiply each number by 100.

3.4   0.25   30.8

_____   _____   _____

3. A shop is offering 20% off all prices. What is the reduction?
You may use a calculator.

Full price: £370   Full price: £585   Full price: £146.50

Reduction _____   Reduction _____   Reduction _____

4. By how much has the temperature dropped?

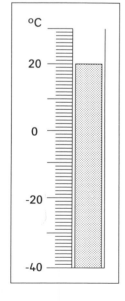   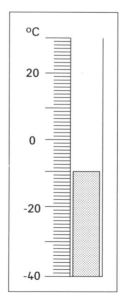

temperature drop = _____   temperature drop = _____

5. Find the total cost of:
8 books costing £6 each _____   6 takes away lunches costing £4 each _____
7 tapes costing £9 each _____   5 packs of drinks costing £4 each _____

6.

18p

C = cost in pence
n = number of cans

C = 18n
If n = 6   C = _____

7. Find $\frac{7}{10}$ of: £1   £5   £10

_____   _____   _____

Find $\frac{3}{4}$ of: £1   £5   £10

_____   _____   _____

8. Two numbers added together equal 28.
They multiply together to equal 195.
What are the two numbers? You may use a calculator.

The numbers are _____ and _____

9.

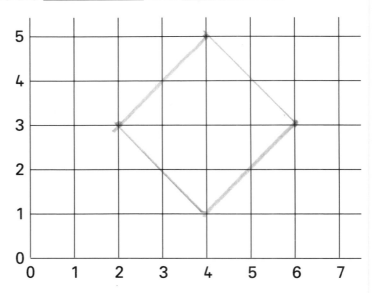

Put these points on the grid and join them up in order.
$(2,3) \longrightarrow (4,5) \longrightarrow (6,3) \longrightarrow (4,1) \longrightarrow (2,3)$

What shape have you drawn? _____

10.

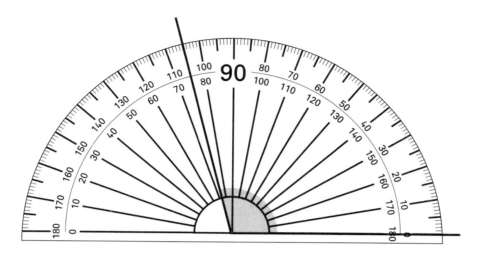

How many degrees does this angle measure? _____

11. Tick the length which is closest to the length of a real bath.

1.7cm   17m   17mm   1.7m   17cm

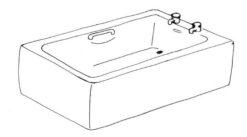

12. What are the readings?

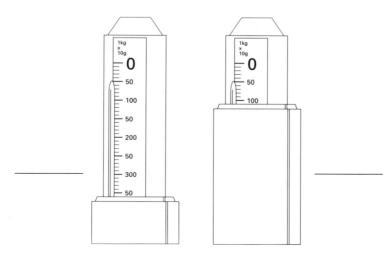

13. Conversion graph: miles and kilometres

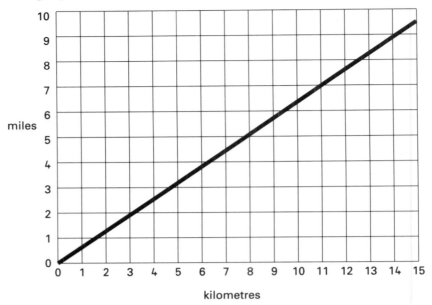

Approximately:

How many miles in 4 km? _____   How many miles in 10 km? _____

How many km in 4 miles? _____   How many km in 8 miles? _____

14. You may use a calculator.
Here are the amounts collected in some collecting tins.

£6·79   £9·15   £8·36   £4·25   £11·75   £6·91

What was the average amount collected to the nearest 10p? _____

15. Map each event to a suitable place on the chance line.

0 = never
1 = always

| You will get heads when tossing a coin. | A new laid egg will break if you drop it. | Hitting your thumb with a hammer hurts. |

A glass marble will float if you put it in water.

Test 1
1. 19-30-46-53-78-87-91
   Check that the child can say the numbers.
2. 10, 9, 6, 8
3. 3, 4, 0, 6
4. total 20p change 30p,
   total 35p change 15p
5. Check that 5 and then 2 circles are coloured.
6. tablespoon: millilitres,
   scales: grams,
   bucket: litres,
   watch: minutes,
   ruler: centimetres
7. There are many possible answers, e.g. 4 − 1, 5 − 2, 6 − 3, 7 − 4, 8 − 5, 9 − 6, 10 − 7.
   Check that the sums work.
8. 21, 19, 17, 15, **13**, **11**, 9, 7, 5, **3**.
   8, 10, **12**, 14, **16**, 18, **20**, 22, 24.
9. A: cylinder, B: cube, C: triangle,
   D: cuboid, E: square,
   F: pentagon
10. A: 1 right angle, B: 2 right angles, C: 3 right angles,
    D: 1 right angle, E: 2 right angles
11. oranges, grapes, 3 children,
    20 children
12.

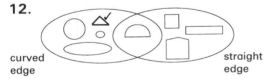

curved edge   straight edge

Test 2
1. 60+8; 40+5; 70+1; 90+6
2. 4+**6**=10; 5+**3**=8; **6**+3=9; **4**+6=10
3. 9−**7**=2; 8−**0**=8; **6**−4=2; **5**−5=0
4. 18p, change 32p; 35p, change 15p
5. Colour a half   Colour a quarter

   Any other solutions
   with 4 sections coloured   or

6. 2,4,6,8,10,12,14,16 ✓
   1,3,5,7,9,11,13,15

7. Any pair of numbers which adds up to 10.
8. A tablespoon measures in millilitres.
   A clock measures in minutes.
   Scales measure in kilograms.
   A bucket measures in litres.
9.

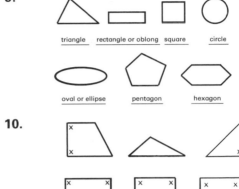

triangle   rectangle or oblong   square   circle

oval or ellipse   pentagon   hexagon

10.

11. 3; January, July and December
12. Tuesday

Test 3
1. 205, 320, 216
2. Any four of the following:
   $2 \times 6 = 12$, $6 \times 2 = 12$,
   $3 \times 4 = 12$, $4 \times 3 = 12$,
   $12 \times 1 = 12$, $1 \times 12 = 12$
3. 3, 4, 5
4. 6, £19·60
5. Check that the estimates are within 1 cm for the 2 cm and 8 cm lines, and within 2 cm for the 12 cm line.
6. 9 cm; 12½ cm; 17½ cm
7. There are many possible answers.
   Check that the sums work.
8. (45) (60) (95) (155) (130)
9. 10, 16
10. They all have right angles.
11. A, C, D
12. £6.50; £5.00

13. 08.30,
    1 hour 45 mins (105 mins)
14. 5.45 or quarter to 6
15. Check the bar graph for accuracy.
    It can be drawn vertically or
    horizontally.

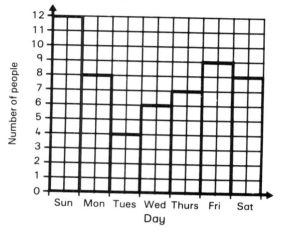

Test 4

1.

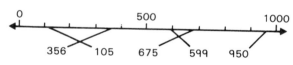

Check that the child can say
the numbers.

2. $20 - 17 = \textbf{3}$, $18 - 15 = \textbf{3}$,
   $15 - 12 = \textbf{3}$, $19 - 14 = \textbf{5}$,
   $20 - 16 = \textbf{4}$, $17 - 13 = 4$
3. 60p, 9p, 30p
4. £2·82, £3·07
5. Check that the estimates are within
   2cm of each line.
6. 20 seconds, 43 seconds,
   64 seconds
7. 1, 2, 3, 1, 2, 3, **1, 2.**
   Tenth number: **1**
   14, 24, 34, 44, 54, **64, 74.**
   Tenth number: **104**
8. 5, 2, 7
9. 45, 18
10. There are several possible ways
    to sort the set, these include:
    spheres/prisms/pyramids,

curved faces/triangle faces/
no curved or triangle faces.
11. Check that the pattern is
    symmetrical and that only three
    colours have been used.
12. Check any 6-sided shape has been
    drawn.
13. Jean, £1·20, 85p
14. Between 50 and 60, Sunday,
    Saturday
15.

Test 5

1. Check that the child can say
   the numbers: 147, 174, 417,
   471, 714, 741.
2. $8 + 7 = \textbf{15}$, $9 + 5 = \textbf{14}$,
   $6 + 8 = \textbf{14}$, $7 + 7 = \textbf{14}$,
   $12 - 5 = \textbf{7}$, $14 - 8 = \textbf{6}$,
   $17 - 9 = \textbf{8}$, $19 - 9 = \textbf{10}$
3. $2 \times 8 = \textbf{16}$, $5 \times 5 = \textbf{25}$,
   $4 \times 3 = \textbf{12}$, $10 \times 8 = \textbf{80}$,
   $7 \times 2 = \textbf{14}$, $10 \times 6 = \textbf{60}$,
   $7 \times 5 = \textbf{35}$, $4 \times 4 = \textbf{16}$
4. 198 miles, 8 gallons
5. 40, 60, 70, 100.
   200, 300, 500, 700.
6.

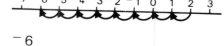

$^-2$

$^-6$

7. $31 + 28 = \mathbf{59}$, $42 + 36 = \mathbf{78}$,
   $16 + 62 = \mathbf{78}$, $45 - 21 = \mathbf{24}$,
   $95 - 21 = \mathbf{74}$, $68 - 53 = \mathbf{15}$
   Check that the child can say
   how they were worked out.

8. 56✓   70✓   83
   66✓   25   120✓
   154✓   170✓

9. 12, 14, 17, 20.
   3, 6, 9, 14.

10. There are several possible ways
    to sort the set, including:
    stars/curves/4-sided shapes

11. A and D

12.
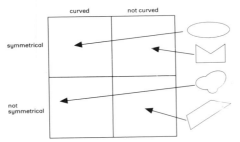

13. Polywebs, Lifers, Jacks

14. 16, April and December,
    August

15.
   | 3 : 25 | or | 15 : 25 |

Test 6

1. 6 275, 25 369.
   Check that the child can say
   the numbers.

2. $8 \times 7 = \mathbf{56}$, $9 \times 9 = \mathbf{81}$,
   $8 \times 8 = \mathbf{64}$, $6 \times 8 = \mathbf{48}$,
   $9 \times 6 = \mathbf{54}$, $7 \times 4 = \mathbf{28}$,
   $9 \times 7 = \mathbf{63}$, $7 \times 7 = \mathbf{49}$

3. 891, 971, 775, 531

4. 21, 1p, 76p

5. 5·20m

6. Check that 3, 6 and then
   9 circles are coloured.

7. 1 metre = 100cm, 1kg = 1 000g,
   1cm = 10mm, 1 litre = 1 000ml

8. 16, 64

9.

In	Out
2	7
5	**13**
7	17

10.
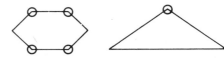

11. Town Hall, F2

12. A, B, D, F

13. 14cm, 18cm, 9cm

14. 1.30m

15. Check that the order chosen is
    sensible e.g. have a meal, make
    my own bed, go on holiday, fly
    to the moon.

Test 7

1. 30 005, 30 050, 30 500, 35 000
   Check that the child can say
   the numbers.

2. $8 \times 7 = \mathbf{56}$, $9 \times 4 = \mathbf{36}$,
   $3 \times 9 = \mathbf{27}$, $6 \times 9 = \mathbf{54}$,
   $75 \times 10 = \mathbf{750}$, $123 \times 10 = \mathbf{1\,230}$,
   $350 \times 10 = \mathbf{3\,500}$

3. 245, 47, 351, 533

4. 270g, 11oz

5. 3mm, 1 684mm (168·4cm)

6. 25p, 60p, £1·25

7. 4·8cm (48mm), 3·4cm (34mm)
   4·1cm (41mm)

8. multiplying by 3,
   5 and 7

9. 8, 5

10.

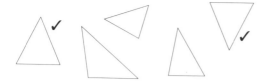

11. A: (1,0), B: (2,2), C: (3,5), D: (5,1)
12. S, H, X, Z
13. B
14. 12cm; 14cm
15. Check that the words chosen are sensible e.g. likely, very unlikely.

Test 8

1. 50 000 + 1 000 + 200 + 6,
   200 000 + 10 000 + 3 000 + 500 + 20,
   700 000 + 20 000 + 3 000 + 500 + 20 + 5
2. $9 + 7 + 6 = \mathbf{22}$,
   $4 + 7 + 5 + 6 = \mathbf{22}$,
   $8 + 8 + 6 + 4 = \mathbf{26}$, $8 \times 6 = \mathbf{48}$,
   $7 \times 9 = \mathbf{63}$, $8 \times 7 = \mathbf{56}$,
   $4 \times 9 = \mathbf{36}$
3. 1 112, 596, 1 023, 226
4. 22, 16p, £2·28
5. 7
6. 370; 1080; 3400
   2500; 8000; 20300
7. 4.09   1.19

8.

9	12	15	18
12	16	20	24

35	40	**45**	50
42	**48**	54	60

16	**20**	24	28
20	25	**30**	35

36	**42**	48	54
42	49	56	**63**

9.

In	Out
8	3
16	7
20	**9**

10. Check B, C, E and Q, R, U have been ticked.

11.

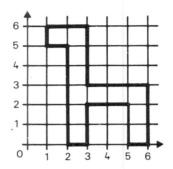

12.

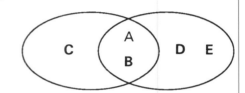

has rotational symmetry   has line symmetry

13. 24, 30, 64

14. Check that the events chosen are sensible.
15. 150; Thursday

Test 9

1.

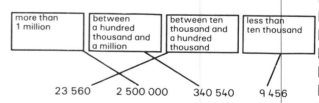

| more than 1 million | between a hundred thousand and a million | between ten thousand and a hundred thousand | less than ten thousand |

23 560   2 500 000   340 540   9 456

2. $700 + 300 \rightarrow 1\,000$
   $900 + 900 \rightarrow 1\,800$

3. 14, 19, 19, 138, 135, 364

4. 30%, 90%, 50%

5. £4·36

6.   0·81m, 1·33m
7. $9 \times 4 = \mathbf{36}$, $8 \times 4 = \mathbf{32}$,
    $7 \times 6 = \mathbf{42}$, $8 \times 8 = \mathbf{64}$,
    $7 \times 100 = \mathbf{700}$,
    $15 \times 100 = \mathbf{1\,500}$,
    $45 \times 100 = \mathbf{4\,500}$

8.   There are several possible ways of describing the pattern, e.g.
    3, 3 + 2, 3 + 2 + 2,
    3 + 2 + 2 + 2.
    Two more sticks have been added to the shape to continue the triangle pattern.

9.

    $4 \xleftarrow{\ (+1 \div 2)\ } 7$
    $15 \xleftarrow{\ (-1 \times 3)\ } 6$
    $10 \xleftarrow{\ (\div 2 + 5)\ } 10$

10.

11.   (4,3),
    (3,2) (3,3) (3,4)
12.   Check that A, D, E and F have been ticked.
13.   Several possible answers from:
    2×12 or 12×2 (P = 28),
    3×8 or 8×3 (P = 22),
    4×6 or 6×4 (P = 20)
14.   10 minutes

15.   fair chance

Test 10

1.   5 664, 8 334, 14 256, 24 769
2. $800 \div 40 = \mathbf{20}$, $600 \div 20 = \mathbf{30}$,
    $900 \div 30 = \mathbf{30}$, $500 \div 10 = \mathbf{50}$
3.   30cm (0·3m), £4·50,
    1 200g (1·2kg),
    250ml (0·25 litre)
4.   23 700, 6 900, 12 300, 56 300.
    44 000, 8 000, 100 000, 456 000.

5.   Allow a little variation in the answers:
    1ft = 30cm, 1kg = $2\frac{1}{4}$lb,
    8km = 5 miles.
6. $2^2 = 4$ $3^2 = 9$
    $5^2 = 25$ $6^2 = 36$
7.   2, 3, 5, 7, 11, 13, 17, 19, 23, 29, 31, 37, 41, 43, 47, 53, 59, 61, 67, 71, 73, 79, 83, 89, 97; prime numbers
8.   3, 5, 9, 10
9. $\frac{3}{6}$, $\frac{4}{6}$, $\frac{15}{20}$, $\frac{30}{100}$, $\frac{12}{15}$
10.   Area=20cm²   Perimeter=18cm
11.   A=(2,3)   B=(6,5)   c=(8,0)
    Check D is 4 along, 5 up
12.

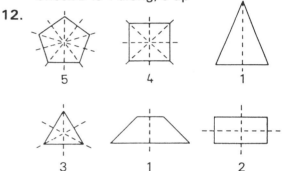

    5   4   1

    3   1   2

13.   65°
14.   5 miles = 8km,
    9 miles = between 14 and 15km,
    6km = $3\frac{1}{2}$ miles,
    17km = $10\frac{1}{2}$ miles
15.   any red card: $\frac{1}{2}$, a club: $\frac{1}{4}$,
    the queen of diamonds: $\frac{1}{52}$

Test 11

1.   26, 23, 18, 16
2. $70 \times 50 = \mathbf{3500}$
    $300 \times 40 = \mathbf{12000}$
    $200 \times 400 = \mathbf{80000}$
3.   50p, 32, 150g
4.   4·46, 0·25, 12·57, 3·20.
    2·5, 2·0, 10·0, 8·2.
5.   120cm, 25mm, 1 500mm, 2 750g, 2 250ml, 200ml
6.   15°C, 15°C

7. 25, 100, square numbers

8. $\frac{5}{10}$, $\frac{6}{12}$.
   $\frac{6}{8}$, $\frac{9}{12}$, $\frac{12}{16}$, $\frac{15}{20}$.

9. $18 \times y$, $46 \div w$, $z \times q$

10. 1440cm³, 2197cm³, 720cm³

11.

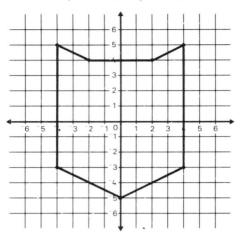

12. A = 122°, B = 36°, C = 66°

13.

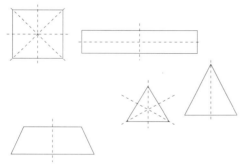

14. more lorries, cars, yes

15. rolling a six: $\frac{1}{6}$, rolling a one: $\frac{1}{6}$,
    rolling an even number: $\frac{3}{6}$

Test 12

1. £33·12, 27p

2. 500 × 50 = **25000**,
   40 × 40 = **1600**,
   800 ÷ 40 = **20**

3. $\frac{2}{3}$ = £8·28, 12% = £2·94,
   $\frac{4}{5}$ = £13, 15% = £9

4. Check that the estimates become
   more accurate: 15%, £125.

5. Accept answers if they are:
   between 30 and 31 miles,
   between $2\frac{1}{2}$ and 3 pints,
   between 8 and 10 ounces.

6. Antarctica, 10°C, 17°C

7. 4, 18, 8, 6

8. 6²=36 7²=49 √25=5 √81=9

9. 7.90; 1.18; 10.75; 2.72

10. Check that the angles are 60° and
    the sides are 65mm.

11. square-4; triangle-1; rectangle-2;
    oval-2; parallelogram-2; trapezium-1

12. 30cm; ½ litre

13. TTT, TTH, THH, HHH

14.

°F	⁻40	32	**50**	140	**212**
°C	⁻40	**0**	10	**60**	100

15. 3, 12, 26

Test 13

1. 5.3(0); 0.4(0); 34.1(0)

2. 340; 25; 3080

3. £74; £117; £29.30

4. 30°; 20°

5. £48 £24
   £63 £20

6. C=108 pence

7. 70p; £3.50; £7
   75p; £3.75; £7.50

8. 13 and 15

9. A square

10. 105°

11. 1.7m

12. 360g; 110g

13. These answers are approximate and
    can vary slightly
    2½ miles; 6½ miles; 6½ km; 12½ km

14. £7.90

15.
```
0                                              1
```
| You will get heads when tossing a coin. | A new laid egg will break if you drop it. | Hitting your thumb with a hammer hurts. |

| A glass marble will float if you put it in water. |